GP Jobs

A Guide to Career Options in General Practice

Mahibur Rahman
MB BCh MSc MRCGP

PUBLICATIONS

with a chapter contributed by **MPS**

ISBN: 978-1-907902-00-0
First published 2010 in Great Britain by

Emedica Publications
Birmingham

0845 388 3402
www.emedica.co.uk

Contents

Career Options for the Qualified GP

Once you complete your GP training there are a variety of career options open to you. In this section we will cover what these options are, with an overview of some of the benefits and drawbacks of each option. More detailed information about some of these options can be found later on in the careers guide.

Conventional GP Careers

The conventional options open to a qualified GP are to work as a freelance GP (locum), to take up a salaried job, to seek a partnership, to work out of hours (OOH), or to combine some of these options with other commitments as a portfolio GP.

Freelance / Locum GP

This is a common starting point for most newly qualified GPs, and many doctors have a successful career working as a freelance GP.

Advantages

Flexibility
As a freelance GP, you can have more control over where and when you work. If you wish to take holidays during school holidays, or go for an extended trip, you are free to do so without needing authorization from anyone else. If you wish to spend 6 months working just a few sessions a week you can. If you need extra money for a specific purpose, you could increase your working week temporarily. If you do not like the way a particular practice works, you can choose not to book more shifts there.

Being self employed
As a locum, you are your own boss. You can set your own rates, and most locums can earn more per day than most salaried GPs. As a self employed contractor rather than an employee, you are also able to claim many more expenses against your tax bill, further increasing your take home pay.

A change is as good as a rest
Sometimes working in different environments, and being able to go in, deal with the patients then leave, without getting involved in internal politics or bureaucracy can be very refreshing. It also allows you a chance to see different ways of working, to take examples of good practice from different places, and also to see what does not work well. Working several sessions as a locum can give you a really good understanding of whether a practice would be a good place to work long term before committing to a salaried position.

Disadvantages

Uncertainty

One of the big drawbacks with working as a locum is living with uncertainty. There is no guarantee that you will be able to work as many sessions as you would like, or that practices will be willing to pay the rates that you had hoped to charge. Currently there are an excess of trained GPs fighting for both salaried posts and locum sessions. Agency locum rates have gone down in the last year in most regions. You may not know exactly how much you will earn from month to month, or exactly where you will work from day to day. For some people this is not really a big issue, but others find it difficult to cope with a variable income when they have large fixed costs to deal with each month (e.g. paying the rent / mortgage, bills, childcare, schooling costs etc.). Some locums will, over time get most of their work from a few regular practices, so that you might have a fairly fixed amount to your income, with the variation limited to the number of additional sessions that are available each month.

Isolation

Being a locum can be very lonely. In many practices, you will arrive for your session, be shown to your room by the practice manager or a receptionist, see 18 patients in 3 hours, then leave, without seeing or talking to any other colleagues. This can be a bit of a shock to newly qualified GPs who have had the regular contact that comes with being in a training practice, as well as the pastoral benefits of being in a VTS group. If you are doing the odd sessions in many different practices, it can be difficult to build relationships with the team.

No employment rights

As a locum, you are a self employed contractor, so you do not have any of the rights a salaried employee would have. This means no paid holidays, no paid study leave, no sick pay, no automatic increase in pay and no job guarantee / entitlement to redundancy pay. Of course you can take this all into account when setting your rates and calculating how much you will have to work in order to make enough to meet all your expenses and still have a decent amount of time for holidays and study leave. You will also need to make provisions to cover your expenses if you are off sick or unable to find work for some time.

Continuing Professional Development / Revalidation

Working as a locum GP can make it more difficult to engage in CPD – for example, you may not have the opportunity to attend weekly clinical meetings or journal clubs. Although the proposals for revalidation are not yet finalised, there are suggestions that it will be more difficult for any GP not working in a managed environment (e.g. salaried / partnership) to meet the requirements for revalidation. Taking part in complete audit cycles for example, can be quite difficult if you are not working regularly in any one practice.

Travelling
In some areas, you may find that you need to be willing to travel quite large distances to ensure that you have enough work. This can lead to increased expenses, increased tiredness and stress if you have to travel in peak times.

Salaried GP

Advantages

Stability
As a salaried GP, you will have a stable work environment, being able to develop a working relationship with members of the team. You will be able to plan your finances as you will have a fixed monthly income. You should have a structured working week, making it easier to plan social engagements, childcare etc. Having a regular workplace also makes it easier to access CPD, to take part in audit and significant event analysis (which are likely to be part of the new revalidation process).

Employment rights
As an employee, you have significant rights. First, you have entitlement to sick pay, a minimum amount of paid annual leave, paternity / maternity pay and leave and unpaid time off for compassionate leave. After working for 2 years in the same employment, you also gain full employment rights including the right to redundancy pay. Usually your past NHS service would be recognised towards this as long as you have not had a break in service. Employment rights are one of the biggest advantages of being an employee.

Fixed commitment
As a salaried GP you should have a job plan outlining your duties, and your work time commitment *should* be fixed. If the practice suddenly needs extra cover, while your employer can request that you do an extra shift, you do not have to accept, and they cannot *demand* that you provide the extra cover. Your main commitment will be to clinical work, and many doctors prefer this – managing other employees, dealing with the upkeep of the building, keeping an eye on the accounts will not be your responsibility.

Disadvantages

Pay
Salaried GP pay is very variable throughout the UK, and even within regions, between practices. The review body recommended range for salaried GP pay for full time doctors (working 9 sessions) is from **£53,781 to £81,158** (2010-2011 figures). These figures apply to doctors working for GMS practices or for PCOs directly. PMS and APMS practices are free to offer any salary they wish. Average pay for salaried GPs in the UK working in either GMS or PMS practices in 2007-2008 (last available actual figures) was £55,790. This figure includes those GPs working on a part time basis.

Average salaried GP pay is about £25k a year less than the average income for a full time partner once GP partners employers NHS pension and National Insurance contributions are taken into consideration.

Workload
The current job market means that employers are in a strong position – there are more qualified GPs than there are salaried jobs available, and in some areas there are very few full time positions available. Unfortunately some employers take advantage of this and start increasing the workload and responsibilities given to the salaried GP until they are working well beyond the scope of their job plan. Some salaried GPs feel unable to refuse extra work, and also feel unable to leave knowing that finding another job may be difficult.

GP Partnerships

Advantages

Control
As a partner, you are responsible for running your own business, and will have a larger degree of control in how the practice is run. You can (in conjunction with the other partners if there are any) decide who to hire, which new services you wish to offer and have a say in how things are organised and run day to day. This can be very satisfying, although it *can* be a burden as well – the buck stops with you.

Pay
GP partners are well paid to reflect the extra responsibility. The latest figures available (2007-2008) showed average pay for a full time GP partner in the UK was £106,072, although there is a significant difference in different regions and according to contract type.

The average income before tax for GP partners in 2007/8, by country was:

- £110,139 in England.
- £91,056 in Northern Ireland.
- £87,371 in Scotland
- £93,366 in Wales.

These figures include both PMS and GMS, and dispensing doctors. It is important to note GP partners have to pay employer's contributions for the NHS pension and employers national insurance contributions, which together account for about 20% of the figures stated here.

The breakdown throughout the whole of the UK according to contract type is:

- £121,753 for GMS **dispensing** GPs.
- £96,189 for GMS **non-dispensing** GPs.
- £132,222 for PMS **dispensing** GPs.
- £113,517 for PMS **non-dispensing** GPs.

Stability
Most partnerships are long term commitments, with many being "a job for life". Being established in one practice for a long time allows you to shape the identity of the practice, to help develop the practice team, and to have continuity of care with patients. It can also make it much easier to plan family commitments, schooling and property purchasing.

Disadvantages

Commitment
Becoming a partner means making a large commitment – both in terms of amount of time per week, expected length of time with the practice and often also financially. Where the building is owned by the partnership, buying in can cost tens of thousands to hundreds of thousands of pounds. This can be a daunting prospect, especially in the current climate where there is no guarantee of a decent return on the property part of the investment. This can also make it much more difficult to leave the partnership or move away if your circumstances change.

Parity
In most partnerships there will be a time period to build up new partners to full parity. A few partnerships will offer full parity straight after a short mutual

evaluation period, but there are still partnerships with a 3 year build up to full parity. This is something that you need to look at in detail before committing.

Employer's responsibilities

As a partner, you will also become an employer, being responsible for the practice team working for you. This can be a cause of stress for many doctors, especially if you have previously only been an employee. The biggest stress occurs when there is a problem – having to dismiss a member of staff, or a dispute within the practice team. Getting to grips with your responsibilities can be a steep learning curve, and your practice manager and the senior partners should be able to help you understand the basics.

Partnership agreements

Something to remember when you take a partnership is that you are running your own business, and are NOT an employee. You have not automatic right to sick pay, holiday pay, study leave, paid maternity leave etc. except whatever is agreed amongst the partners. Each partnership can set their own rules – in some practices for example, short periods of sickness will be deducted from your annual leave entitlement. In some practices, women will be offered a set period of paid maternity leave, while others offer none, with the partner having to fund their own locum to cover them during this period. It is *really* important that you make sure that you have a partnership agreement and that you understand and agree to it. Partnership disputes and dissolutions can be *very* stressful and *very* costly.

Out of Hours GP (OOH GP)

Advantages

Money

Working full time as an OOH GP can be very lucrative, with some jobs for working 40 hours a week OOH paying as much as £130k with good benefits.

Flexibility

Many doctors do some OOH work to top up their salary, with the flexibility to do a few extra shifts in busy periods to get some extra income.

Job satisfaction

Dealing with acute primary care problems can be satisfying. Although there is a lot of routine work that comes through to the OOH centre, successfully treating sick patients on a home visit can be very rewarding. A lot of doctors also enjoy the chance to focus on clinical work, and not deal with QOF, and the extra bureaucracy that often comes with routine daytime GP work.

Disadvantages

Unsocial hours
By the nature of OOH work, you will be working a lot of unsocial hours – evenings, weekends, nights. If you are working OOH full time, this can mean that you are working when your family, friends and colleagues might be free. If you are working a lot of overnight shifts, this can be very tiring and mess up your body clock.

Higher risk of litigation
Several studies have shown that patients are more likely to sue a doctor other than their usual GP. This means that you are more likely to have to deal with a complaint as an OOH GP.

Deskilling
Working full time OOH means that there are some illnesses and conditions that you are unlikely to deal with – chronic disease management, for example. Over time this can lead to deskilling and make it more difficult for you to start back in routine daytime practice.

Portfolio GP

A portfolio GP has more than one type of job making up their working week. This may involve working part time in any of the options mentioned so far (partner, salaried, OOH, locum) with a variety of additional roles in the portfolio. Additional roles could be anything, and some of the more popular roles include working as a forensic medical examiner, prison doctor, medicolegal work, occupational health or being involved in medical education.

Some of these options will be looked at in more detail in a later chapter on portfolio GPs.

Alternative GP Careers

Some doctors choose to pursue an alternative GP job – either as a career choice, or as a temporary post to experience something different. This can include working as a cruise ship doctor, working as an MOD doctor, or international work. In this section we will have a brief look at some of these options, what they entail, and how to go about pursuing them.

Cruise Ship doctor

This is definitely not a career choice for everyone, but for the right person it can offer an opportunity to see the world, to have a varied and challenging workload while offering good support for CPD. All cruise ships must have a medical team onboard, with most ships carrying 2 doctors (some larger vessels have more) as well as a team of nurses.

The work is a mixture of general practice and emergency work; with most ships having a well kitted out medical centre – ultrasound, X-ray, lab investigations, defibrillators and in-patient treatment beds and rooms available.

You do need to be able to make decisions quickly, sometimes with the responsibility of having to turn the ship around to go back to the last port if someone needs emergency treatment beyond what can be offered on board.

A qualified GP would also need to have up to date qualifications in ALS and having paediatric life support certification (APLS) as well would be a great help.

P&O Princess is the biggest employer, covering some of the major cruise ships operated by P&O, Cunard, Ocean Village, and Princess Cruises.

Work patterns can vary, but usually you would have 2 or more surgeries a day (a bit like in a GP surgery), with on call commitments for the rest of the time. Where there are 2 doctors on board, this would usually be shared, with you doing a 24 hour on call on a 1 in 2 basis, either as first or second on call. Responsibilities include looking after the health of all staff on board as well as the passengers.

The minimum commitment required is usually for 2 tours lasting 4 months each. Usually you would have between 4-8 weeks holiday in between each tour. This type of work is especially suitable for single doctors as you will be away for long periods at a time. After the first 2 months, it may be possible to get family to come on board at a discounted price to visit.

The work is reasonable well paid – currently P&O Princess pay the gross equivalent of about £67-70k for 243 days worked – this leaves you with about 17 weeks annual leave! While on board, you have minimal expenses – your food, accommodation and uniform are all paid for by the cruise company. On top of this, in the UK, if you are at sea for more than 183 days a year, you can receive your salary tax free.

Drawbacks to being a ships doctor can include long periods on board without being able to go ashore (as you may be on call). Isolation from family and friends – you may well miss important events and anniversaries – there is no option to "have a weekend off" during your tour. Finally, not everyone is suited to life on the sea, and if you suffer badly from seasickness, this is probably not the job for you!

Further reading:

P&O Ships doctors – **www.shipsdoctors.com**

Shafi S (1998) Working as a ship's doctor – BMJ 7130 Volume 316 available online at **www.bmj.com/cgi/content/full/316/7130/S2-7130**

Ministry Of Defence Doctor

All three main branches of the military in the UK are actively recruiting GPs. There are two main ways to work within this field – as a medical officer, or as a civilian medical practitioner. If you choose to enter as a medical officer, then you can expect to undergo basic officer training lasting from several weeks to a few months – the exact length will depend on whether you are joining the Army, the Royal Navy, or the Royal Air Force (if you want to join the Royal Marines, then it is even longer!).

Joining as a medical officer usually means making a minimum commitment of 3 years. As a civilian medical practitioner you do not need to sign up for a minimum commitment period.

For those that are happy to work in a highly disciplined and regimented environment, the training offered and benefits are excellent. Pay is better than most top end salaried GP posts, although perhaps not as high as some of the best performing partnerships, currently ranging from about £80-120k per year depending on which service, and your level of experience. Support for CPD and ongoing training is excellent, with much larger study budgets than you would be offered in most salaried posts. As an officer, you are also eligible to access the benefits of the Officer's mess – which can include very high standards of food and access to excellent sporting and social facilities.

You may be posted abroad as part of your duties, and this may involve being away from home for long periods. Many see this opportunity to work overseas as a benefit.

The downsides are that you will have to be willing to wear a uniform if you go in as an officer, and as you will be seeing a skewed population (largely young, fit patients), you may become deskilled in dealing with paediatrics, and some of the issues more commonly seen in older patients.

International work

Working overseas for a period has been an attractive option to many doctors wishing to combine work with a chance to travel. With the current difficulty in securing full time work, many newly qualified GPs are considering going to work abroad for a few years or even permanently as a serious option. Working in a different healthcare system can help you to gain new skills, and to see different ways of working. Having a UK CCT and MRCGP will open a lot of doors in terms of working as a GP abroad. The most common locations for UK trained GPs to work overseas at the moment are Australia, New Zealand, Canada and the Middle East. While most doctors that go to work abroad do so with a view to earning a decent income as well as learning new skills, some choose to do humanitarian work.

Many doctors want to travel, but are limited by the amount of time off available in many standard salaried positions. Since the advent of *Modernising Medical Careers* (MMC) it has become increasingly difficult to take time out of a training programme to travel, and certainly in general practice, it is no longer possible to shorten your rotation by recognising previous experience overseas. Working abroad *after* your CCT can allow you to spend time travelling, while earning a decent wage. Once you have a CCT and MRCGP, many countries will allow you to work without taking any further examinations – you will have to register with the appropriate national medical council.

The pay is variable depending on which country you work in – it can range from a little less than an average salaried GP in the UK to similar or even a little higher. Where the nominal salary is lower, the benefits are usually greater – for example, salaries in the Middle East range from about £50k - £75k, but are usually paid tax free, with furnished accommodation of a high standard provided, as well as a car allowance and private school fees paid for children. Most contracts also include a tax free bonus for every full year worked.

In Australia and New Zealand, the pay is often a mixture of a fixed basic pay with extra payment for each patient seen or on a fee for service basis (i.e. the more you do, the more you get paid). Many GPs also cover local hospitals on an on call rota as a *Visiting Medical Officer*, and this attracts an extra fee. Pay rates vary depending on where the practice is, the workload, your additional skills, and how many patients you see, but many jobs pay between $175k - $275k Australian per year (£100k - £160k with exchange rate as of June 2010). Many of these jobs include airfare and accommodation provided.

In Canada, there are various provinces that each has their own licensing procedures. Many have a large shortage of available GPs, and these include British Columbia, Alberta and Manitoba. Pay for a GP is based on a basic pay + fee for service model, and vary hugely with area and workload – if you can offer cover for emergency services or obstetrics you will be able to earn significantly more. Income (depending a lot on the amount of fee for service work you can or wish to do) can range between $160k - $300k + Canadian (around £105k - £195k + with exchange rates as of June 2010).

Completing all the paperwork needed to take up a paid position overseas can be quite time consuming, and usually you will need to make a minimum time commitment of between 6 months and a year.

The exact requirements for different countries varies greatly, and is beyond the scope of this guide, but the following sources offer more detailed guidance and information for specific regions.

Australia

Details on registration to work as a GP in Australia:
www.health.gov.au/internet/otd/Publishing.nsf/Content/work-Standard%20pathway

New Zealand

Details on types of registration and requirements for working in NZ:
www.mcnz.org.nz/Registration/Howtobecomearegistereddoctor/tabid/71/Default.aspx

An agency that can offer advice and help in finding a GP position in Australia or New Zealand is Ochre Recruitment:
www.ochrerecruitment.com.au

Canada

Information about licensing, with links to the relevant council for each of the six Canadian provinces:
www.srpc.ca/canlocum.html

Government funded recruitment agency for medical vacancies in British Columbia:
www.healthmatchbc.org

Manitoba Healthcare recruitment:
www.healthemployment.ca

Humanitarian Work

For those doctor looking to put their medical skills to use overseas in the developing world, there are opportunities to spend time working in areas of need. The nature of the work can range from manning makeshift health camps / clinics in refugee camps, to helping train local healthcare workers to working with communities with coping with the effects of HIV / AIDS. You could be working in any continent – from an inner city posting in India to a rural village in Ghana.

Undertaking this type of work can help you share your skills and knowledge, allow you to gain management experience and see a different spectrum of illness than you might be used to in the UK, as well as make friendships that will last a lifetime.

There are various organisations that may be able to offer posts for trained GPs, with 2 of the most popular and well known being Médecins Sans Frontières (MSF), and Voluntary Service Overseas (VSO). Once a suitable placement is found, the organisation will help in completing the necessary paperwork to allow you to travel and work. Both MSF and VSO will pay for travel, accommodation and offer a small stipend to cover living and other expenses will abroad. MSF postings usually require you to be away for between 9 and 12 months. MSF usually require a minimum commitment of 1 year, with many postings being of 2 years duration.

If you are interested in doing humanitarian work but cannot commit to this kind of timescale, then you may be able to help by volunteering on a project with Doctors Worldwide (DWW). DWW have a need for volunteers for ongoing projects all over the world, as well as short term help for relief operations after natural disasters. The minimum time spent on a project can be as short as 3 weeks. Volunteers pay for their own travel expenses with DWW, but living expenses and food once on site are provided. There is no stipend paid by DWW.

Further details:

Médecins Sans Frontières – **www.msf.org**

Voluntary Service Overseas – **www.vso.org**

Doctors Worldwide – **www.doctorsworldwide.org**

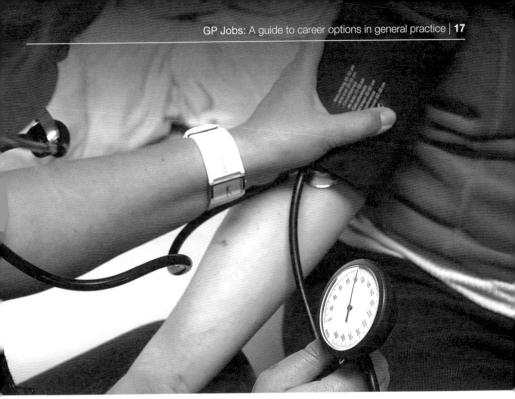

How to succeed as a locum GP

Many doctors spend some, or their entire career working as a locum GP in some capacity. This section will look at some of the key considerations if you wish to succeed in this type of work.

Starting out as a locum

When starting out as a locum GP, you need to consider the different options for how you might arrange your locum work, get your documentation in order, write you terms and conditions, put together a system to keep track of invoices and pension forms, and keep detailed records for tax purposes.

Documentation

Whether you arrange locums yourself or work via a locum agency, you will need to put together a pack of key documents. At a minimum this will need to include:

- A brief Curriculum Vitae (CV)
- CCT or CEGPR
- GMC registration and license to practice
- Enhanced CRB check (disclosure)
- Indemnity cover for GP non principal work to cover number of sessions you intend to work
- Performers list inclusion letter
- Immunisations – Hep B, Hep C, +/- Varicella, Rubella
- Minimum of 2 recent references
- Proof of eligibility to work in UK (EU passport / visa status)

Options for locum work

There are three main options for doing locum work – arranging your own sessions, arranging work via a locum agency, and working with other locums through a locum chambers.

Self arranged locums

Arranging locum work yourself involves the most legwork, but offers the most reward. With this route you would directly offer your own services to practices. This would mean that you would handle your own paperwork – advertising your availability, arranging sessions, setting rates and conditions, and invoicing.

When starting out, it can take some time to build up a list of regular practices that will offer you sessions. The benefits of arranging work yourself include the ability to set your own terms and conditions and your own rates. Usually it is possible to charge more than you would be paid per hour working via an agency as there are no agency fees for the practice to pay. Any work for NHS practices arranged directly is pensionable in the NHS scheme.

A good way to start getting some sessions is to put together a brief CV and write a good covering letter explaining your past GP experience. If you are just finishing a training scheme, you should include details of your VTS and the practice(s) where you worked as a registrar. Include a summary of your terms and conditions and your rates, as well as your contact details. You could then post this out to all the practices in the areas you are willing to work in. You can get contact details of all practices from the NHS Choices website (**www.nhs.uk**) this allows you to search within a set distance from your home postcode.

Agency locum

Another option for getting locum sessions is to register with a locum agency to find you work. You may choose to register with more than one agency to increase the amount of work open to you. A major benefit of arranging work this way is that you do not have to hunt for sessions – the agency will normally have sessions available and contact you. You also will not need to produce invoices, but will usually get timesheets completed by the practice manager or a senior receptionist at each practice after completing a session. When you are starting out as a locum, this is sometimes a way to get some shifts fairly quickly to get you started.

The disadvantages include lower rates, with less room for negotiation – many agencies pay a fixed rate per hour.

Agencies will have their own terms and conditions, and many include a restrictive covenant – for example stating that if you take a substantive post in any practice that you first worked at via the agency, the practice will need to pay an agency fee. Covenants usually restrict you from contracting to do sessions at practices directly for a set period (e.g. 6 months).

Finally, if you contract to do sessions via an agency, this work is *not* usually pensionable under the NHS scheme.

Locum Chambers

A more recent development and becoming increasingly popular is for a group of locums to work together via a locum chambers. In effect the individual members are all self employed locums, who pay for chambers staff to manage bookings, invoices, expenses and help with accounting.

Members of chambers would usually pay either a fixed fee each month to cover the costs of employing a manager, or a proportion of each invoice would be kept aside to cover these costs. Letting the chambers manage all the non clinical aspects of locum work can free the locums to focus on clinical work and continuing professional development.

All members of chambers remain self employed, so the work is pensionable under the NHS scheme – this can be a big advantage over working via an agency.

Members of the same chambers will often have the same rates and terms and conditions, and by working together, it can sometimes allow flexibility in terms of finding a replacement for a session at short notice if an emergency or illness occurs.

Perhaps the biggest advantage of working via chambers is the peer support and sharing of experience that can come from such an arrangement. A common part of most chambers includes regular educational meetings organised by the chambers for the benefit of members. With the onset of revalidation looming, this will become even more important.

This approach was pioneered in the UK by Pallant Medical Chambers, and has now been adopted by various groups of freelance GPs throughout the country.

Further reading:

Pallant Medical Chambers - **www.pallantmedical.co.uk**

Setting and using terms and conditions

If you arrange locums yourself, then it is important that you set and use your own terms and conditions. Your terms and conditions should set out what *is* and *is not* covered when you are offering sessions, details of the acceptable timeframe for payment of invoices, charges, number of patients to be seen per hour or in a session, home visits etc. There is no set format for terms and conditions, but you should try to achieve a balance between covering most eventualities and having a document that is clear and easy to understand. Having terms and getting the practice to agree to them before you accept a booking will protect you in case of a dispute arising after the work has been done.

Some of the key areas to consider including in your terms and conditions are:

Rates
Price per session, standard hourly rate, on call rate, extended hours rate (if different). Some locums have a price for whole day or half day cover.

Appointment times / rest periods
A sensible clause is to specify at least 10 minutes per appointment – remember as a locum you may be unfamiliar with the practice, local referral policies etc. and may need a little longer than the regular team to practice in a safe way. For sessions of 3 hours or longer, you might want to specify a 10 minute break in the middle of the surgery.

Administration time
How much time do you need for administrative tasks generated by the surgery? This could include referrals, completing any relevant forms or any other admin required by the practice that you are happy to do – such as repeat prescriptions.

Visits policy
Specify if you are willing to do visits, and if so, whether you will charge an hourly rate, or charge per visit. Remember to include time to return to the surgery afterwards to input the details into the medical record. This is very important for the accuracy of the records, but also for your own protection.

Overrun / extras policy
You should specify how you will deal with any overrun – will you charge extra, will you allow a certain amount of extra time without charge. Will you be happy to see extras – if so, whether these will be charged on an hourly basis or per extra patient.

Payment policy + penalties
You should specify when you will invoice the practice and when (and how) you expect to be paid (cheque, bank transfer). There is no set time period, but 14 days or 28 days are commonly used. Some locums request payment by cheque on the day of the shift. You should include details of any penalties for late payment of invoices.

Cancellation policy

State what would happen in case of cancellation by the practice or by the locum (you). You may wish to have a sliding scale covering cancellation depending on the amount of notice the practice provides. This will protect you in case of cancellation with short notice, where you may have turned down other work, and might find it difficult to replace the sessions.

An example set of terms and conditions is given on the next page – please note this is a sample – your own terms may be more or less detailed, and could include anything that you feel is reasonable.

Bear in mind that if your terms are too onerous, or impose too many restrictions on the practice, you may have bookings turned down. Good terms and conditions will be fair to the practice while offering you reasonable work conditions and protection should the workload vary significantly from the initial agreement.

Terms and Conditions for Locum GP Cover bookings

Bookings: All bookings must be confirmed in written form (via email or fax) – once confirmation is received, the booking is considered a firm contract on both parties, and an acceptance of these terms and conditions.

Appointments: All appointments must be a minimum of 10 minutes long. The last appointment should be booked to FINISH at the end time. E.g. if you have booked me to work until 6pm, the last appointment should begin no later than 5.50pm.

Extras: If you would like me to see extra patients (over and above the number booked in) I am usually happy to do so, and I will charge at my usual hourly rate in 15 minute increments.

Home visits: I am happy to do home visits if they are booked in advance (at the time of the booking). These will be charged according to time taken at hourly rate. The time will include time taken to attend and assess the patient, travel time back to the surgery and time to enter the details of the visit into the patient records.

Full day / on call cover: Charged at standard hourly rate

Extended Hours / Weekends: Please call to discuss availability / price

Cancellation by the practice: If the practice needs to cancel a booking, you will need to inform me as soon as possible in written form (via email or fax). A cancellation fee will apply according to the notice period given for cancellation as follows:

Cancellation 31 days or more before a booking – no charge.
Cancellation 30 - 15 days before a booking – 50% of fee payable.
Cancellation 15 days or less before a booking – full fee remains payable.

Cancellation by the locum: In the unlikely event that I am unable to provide cover as booked at short notice (e.g. due to emergency), I will inform you as soon as practical, and I will endeavour to find a suitable replacement.

Payment: I will invoice you for all work done within 2 weeks of providing the cover (usually sooner). All invoices should be paid within 28 days via bank transfer or cheque.

Invoices

You will need to produce invoices in order to get paid for locum work that you do on a self employed basis. There is no set format for this, although there are some key pieces of information that should be included as a minimum. You can create simple invoices using any word processor or using Microsoft Excel. There are specialist software packages that can be used to produce slick looking invoices, although this is not necessary. You also need to have a system to keep track of which invoices you have sent, which have been paid and any which are overdue and need chasing.

Some key information to include in your invoices includes:

Your details
Your name and address details, so that they know who they are paying!

Invoice date and reference
The invoice date is very important for tax purposes, you may wish to include your own reference to make it easier to track which invoices have been paid etc. This is especially helpful if you have sent more than one invoice to the same practice (e.g. for different shifts).

Client details (name / address)
You should detail who the client is – this will be the surgery, the PCO or might be the OOH company.

Sessions covered
You should include a breakdown of each session or period covered by the invoice, with details of the rate per hour or rate per session applied.

Extras / visits
If you have separate charges for extra and visits, these should be detailed.

Invoice total
The total to be paid for the invoice should be easy to see – you might make this bold, or underline it to make it obvious.

Payment period and details
You should include details of the timescale for payment of the invoice, as well as details for payment – who should the cheque be made payable to? If you want to be paid by bank transfer, you could include your banking details.

Always save a copy of any invoice created for your accounting records and to allow you to check that the amount paid matches the invoice amount.

Sample Invoice for Locum Work

INVOICE

Dr V G Locum
112 Acacia Avenue, Anytown, AN1 6BJ

Client: Goodtown Health Centre, GT4 4HQ

Invoice number: GTHC/08/01
Invoice date: **1 August 2010**
Invoice period: July 2010

Date	Item	Rate (£)	Number	Total (£)
06.07.2010	Surgery (hourly)	80.00	2	160.00
06.07.2010	Home visits	40.00	2	80.00
12.07.2010	Half day	300.00	1	300.00
15.07.2010	Full day	600.00	1	600.00
18.07.2010	Surgery (Hourly)	80.00	3	240.00
			Total	1380.00

Total for this invoice: **£1380.00**

Terms:
Payment by BACS or cheque within 14 days

Cheques should be made payable to "Dr V G Locum"

Banking details:
Account name: V G Locum
Sort code: 40-00-01
Account number: 55555555

Locum Tax and accounts

When you start out as a locum, you will need to register with HM Revenue & Customs (HMRC) as being self employed. You need to do this even if you are going to work via locum agencies as most of them pay you without deducting taxes and National Insurance. You have 3 months from the date you first become self employed to register, or you will have to pay a fine.

National Insurance

You will have to pay Class 2 National Insurance contributions as soon as you become self employed. Currently this is at a rate of £2.40 a week (Tax year 2010-2011), and can be paid either monthly by direct debit or quarterly in arrears.

Income Tax

You will be invoicing practices and getting paid **gross** i.e. without any deductions for tax and national insurance. You will therefore need to keep detailed records of all your income and expenses and complete a self assessment (tax return) after the end of the tax year.

It is therefore essential to budget for your tax bill – you should keep about a third of your income aside separately to pay your tax bill. After your first year of being self employed you will also have to start paying taxes on account based on your previous year's earnings (paying an estimated figure in advance). These payments will be made twice a year, rather than annually. This means that your tax bill after your first full year as a locum will be larger than in subsequent years (as you will have to pay the previous years bill + half of the projected bill for the following year).

It is definitely worth getting a good accountant to deal with your taxes – they will save you a lot of time, stress and probably save you more money than they will charge you for doing your accounts.

VAT

This is an area of confusion amongst many new locums. Usually any business that has a turnover above £70,000 has to register for VAT and charge VAT on all invoices. Medical services (which include locum work) are exempt from VAT, so you *do not* need to register for VAT or charge VAT on your invoices for locum work.

You would only need to register for VAT if your income from work that is *not* exempt from VAT (such as Medico-legal work) is above £70,000. Even if this was the case, your locum work would still remain exempt. Any decent accountant will understand the exemptions and be able to advise you accordingly.

Expenses

Keep detailed records and receipts for all expenses that you incur as part of providing your locum services. Claiming all the appropriate expenses will make a huge difference in the total amount of pay you have, and your total tax bill. As a self employed locum you can claim all expenses that are 'wholly and exclusively incurred' as part of your business. The following information is correct in *general* at the time of going to print, but you should contact a qualified accountant to check exactly what you can claim for given your own circumstances.

Expense that can usually be claimed can include (but are not limited to):

Car expenses
You should keep a record of all your business mileage – as a locum this includes travel from your home to any practice as well as all visits. You can either keep a log throughout the year to get an exact business mileage, or keep a detailed log of your private mileage vs. business mileage over a representative period (e.g. 1 month). You could then apply this proportion to your total annual mileage and claim a proportion of all your car running costs (insurance, road tax, servicing), as well as claiming costs for mileage. Currently you can claim 40 pence per mile tax free for any mileage up to 10,000 miles.

Indemnity
This is a major expense for most locums – if you are working full time as a locum, expect to pay over £5000 per year for indemnity.

Administration
Throughout the year you will spend lots of small amounts on things like stationary, stamps, printing that will add up. All of these costs can be offset against your tax bill. You will need to print and post out CVs, invoices, etc. If you are going to purchase a computer or printer to aid the running of your locum business, a proportion can usually be claimed for business use.

Subscriptions and memberships

You can claim for all job related subscriptions and relevant memberships. This includes GMC registration and licensing fees, membership of the RCGP or BMA and subscriptions to any journals.

Use of home for running your business

As a locum you may do your invoicing, accounting, marketing and paperwork from home. You can usually claim a proportion of your home running costs for business use (this can include a proportion of the rent and sometimes bills). This is a complex area, and you should consult an accountant to get an understanding of what you can claim.

Pension

Some locum work is pensionable under the NHS scheme – it depends largely on how you contract to do the work, and on the status of the practice or organisation that you are working for. A summary is given on the next page.

- Self employed, self arranged locum work for NHS practices – pensionable
- Self employed, chambers arranged locum work for NHS practices – pensionable
- Self employed locum work in non NHS practices – not pensionable
- Agency locum work – not usually pensionable regardless of practice type
- Work done via a limited company - not usually pensionable regardless of practice type

In order for you to pension appropriate locum forms, you will need to complete form GP Locum A (and get it signed by each practice) and a GP Locum B each month and pay your contribution to the Primary Care Organisation where you did that work. The PCO will then pay the employer's contribution.

You will need to complete a separate Locum A form for *each* practice in which you worked that month, and a single Locum B form for the whole month to cover all practices in each PCO that you are claiming for. Examples of both forms are shown in the next 2 pages.

GP LOCUM A

NHS Pension Scheme - GP Locum's certificate of GMS, PMS or APMS NHS work and pay for one NHS GP Practice, PCT or LHB

GENERAL GUIDANCE

GP Locum: To claim NHS Scheme membership for GP Locum GMS, PMS or APMS NHS work, please complete Part 1 of this form and send with the monthly invoice to the appropriate NHS Pension Scheme Employing Authority (i.e. a GP Practice, PCT or LHB). A separate form is required for each payment.

Only NHS GP Locum services contracted directly between an Individual GP Locum and a NHS Pension Scheme Employing Authority (EA), covering for an absent GP(s) or working on a temporary basis, may be entered on this form. A GP Locum who sets themselves up as a limited company cannot be pensionable in the NHS Pension Scheme. Do NOT use this form to record OOHs - use form GP SOLO.

Part1. To be completed by the GP Locum

Your name

National Insurance number

Host PCT / LHB

Host PCT/LHB Registration No. If supplied

Please enter below the dates you worked for the Employing Authority (i.e. Practice).

From   /   /   to   /   /   From   /   /   to   /   /

From   /   /   to   /   /   From   /   /   to   /   /

Signature

Date   /   /

I claim NHS Pension Scheme membership for the NHS work I undertook, (which is named in Part 2 below) as an individual; not as a limited company.

Part 2 To be completed by the Employing Authority (EA) Authorised Signatory
(eg. practice manager, PCT, payroll manager) The same person cannot sign Parts 1 & 2.

GP Locum's gross pay for the NHS work shown in Part 1 above.   £

Which GP(s) was this work done for?

Name(s)

EA code

EA stamp

Declaration
I certify that this EA has paid the GP Locum the gross amount shown for the NHS work declared in Part 1.

Signature

Date of payment   /   /

GP LOCUM B

	GPLocum own use only

NHS Pension Scheme - GP Locum's monthly record
of GMS / PMS / APMS pay
and pension contributions

Personal Details

Surname	Other names		Sex (M/F)	Date of birth
NI number	NHSPS ref number	Host PCT / LHB	Host PCT / LHB Ref. no.	
Address			Calendar Month & Year	

Tiered Contribution Rate

*Tick one box (see overleaf for guidance)   5% ☐   6.5% ☐

PART 1   7.5% ☐   8.5% ☐

Employing Authority code	Name of Practice, PCT or LHB	First day worked for this payment	Last day worked for this payment	Date gross pay received	Gross Pay £	p

PART 2

For PCT / LHB use only

Total Contributions	
Employee	£
Employer	£

Total of gross NHS locum pay		a
Professional expenses deduction (a x 10%)		b
Net NHS pensionable pay (a - b)		c
NHS Pension Scheme gross employee contributions (c x 5%, 6.5%, 7.5%, 8.5%)		d
Total of any NHS Pension Scheme % added years contributions (c x %)		e
Total of any NHS extra % MPAVCs (c x % or agreed sum)		f
Grand total of NHS Pension Scheme employee contributions (d + e + f)		g

IMPORTANT: *Now attach a cheque to this form, payable to your Host PCT / LHB, for the total amount at (g) above and send it to arrive no later than the 7th day of the month, following the month this form relates to. You must attach a properly completed form GP Locum A for every payment declared on this record. *REMEMBER: If you have paid tiered contributions at the wrong rate, you must liaise with the PCT / LHB in respect of any arrears.If you have relocated you must contact your previous PCT / LHB in respect of arrears.*

GP Locum B - (V2) 4/2009   1

GP Locum Rates

Setting rates is often a difficult process. When working for agencies, they usually quote a fixed rate, although if you are needed to cover a session at short notice, you may be able to negotiate a better rate.

When arranging your own locums you can usually pitch you rates slightly higher than the rates that agencies are offering and still be cheaper to the practice.

It is illegal to collude with other locums to agree rates that you will all charge. Doing so could lead to you being found to have formed a cartel, with severe penalties (up to 10% of your turnover for 3 years). This does not mean that you cannot discuss your rates with your colleagues, or find out how much agencies are paying locally.

When setting rates, you can charge in a variety of ways:

- Hourly rate for standard daytime work
- Hourly rate for extended hours
- Rate for half or full days – specify what this includes
- On call rate
- Rates for visits – hourly, or for each visit
- Rates for seeing extras – per extra or according to time

When setting rates for surgeries or charging an hourly rate, it is important to state clearly how much administration time you will need and be charging for. For example, if doing a 3 hour surgery, you might need a further 20-30 minutes to complete the necessary relevant paperwork for those patients.

Many OOH providers offer standardised rates for OOH locums which is often lower than many agency daytime rates – this reflects the fact that currently many OOH providers have a surplus of doctors looking for OOH shifts – some areas have a waiting list!

If you are trying to calculate an annual income from your average weekly locum earnings, you need to consider the fact that you will need time off for continuing professional development, annual leave, possibly sick leave, and that you may not be offered any work during bank holidays (as OOH providers often offer these shifts to their regular doctors first).

You need to balance the amount that you charge with the amount of work that you are getting based on that rate – if you have higher charges, you might work a bit less, but still make the same money as someone working more hours at a lower rate. Another way to look at this is to consider how much you wish to earn, and then you could work out how many hours or sessions you will need to work at different rates to achieve this.

So to calculate your annual income, you should take your average weekly income and multiply it by 42, 43, or 44 depending on how much leave you intend to take:

- 6 weeks leave (4 weeks annual / 1 week study / 1 week sick) + 2 weeks bank holidays = 44 working weeks
- 7 weeks leave, (5 weeks annual / 1 week study / 1 week sick) + 2 weeks bank holidays = 43 working weeks
- 8 weeks leave, (6 weeks annual / 1 week study / 1 week sick) + 2 weeks bank holidays = 42 working weeks

Rate setting examples

Hourly Rate	Hours worked	Weekly Pay	Annual income		
			8 weeks leave	7 weeks leave	6 weeks leave
£65	36	£2340	£98,280	£100,620	£102,960
£70	33	£2310	£97,020	£99,330	£101,640
£75	31	£2325	£97,650	£99,975	£102,300
£80	29	£2320	£97,440	£99,760	£102,080

Sessional Rate	Sessions Worked	Weekly Pay	Annual Income		
			8 weeks leave	7 weeks leave	6 weeks leave
£250	9	£2250	£94,500	£96,750	£99,000
£275	8	£2200	£92,400	£94,600	£96,800
£300	7	£2100	£88,200	£90,300	£92,400
£325	6	£1950	£81,900	£83,850	£85,800

Tips for locum success

Put together a professional locum pack

Having all your paperwork in order, and making it easy for practices to check all your documentation will make it easier for them to hire you. A good way to do this is to scan all your paperwork and combine them into a single document – ideally in PDF format. You could then email this to locum agencies or practices that wanted to book you.

Balance agency with self arranged work

When you are starting out, you might find that registering with one or two agencies helps you to get some shifts early on. Arranging your own work may involve more legwork, but long term it will pay off.

Terms and conditions are essential

Writing and using sensible terms and conditions will protect you in case there is ever a dispute about charges and what is or is not covered – they are essential.

Set your rates carefully, be flexible

Deciding on what rates you wish to charge is a delicate balance – too low and you could be short selling yourself, too high, and you might lose work. A good rule of thumb is to see what agencies will offer you in a region and work from there.

Get to know the practice manager and receptionists

Sending out your CV is a good way to get started, but if you can make an appointment to see a few practice managers, you are more likely to be remembered. When doing locum sessions, make sure you talk to the receptionists, and try to pop in and see the practice manager. Putting a name to a face really helps when they are making decisions on who to offer a shift to first.

Send out your CV locally, and to PCT / LHB, and LMC

Send out your CV with a good covering letter to all the practices within a commutable distance – and then send it out again a few months later. Often a practice manager will offer shifts to the last person that wrote to them – as the details are handy when they are thinking about locums. Many PCOs and LMCs will have a list of locums available in the region that they circulate regularly to practices – get your name on the list and you might be offered the odd shift.

Always be punctual, professional and polite

The 3 Ps will get you remembered and get you asked back to practices.

Make sure you always arrive in good time – you should aim to be at least 10-15 minutes early the first time you are at a practice so you can meet the team, familiarise yourself with the room and the call system, find out where the toilets are, and settle in before you start.

Behave professionally with both patients and staff, and ensure all your dealings show you in a professional light. This starts with sending our professional looking CVs and covering letters, confirming all bookings in writing, invoicing correctly and promptly, and extends to having a professional appearance when you turn up for surgery, and ensuring you have all the correct equipment to do the job.

Be polite in all your dealings – again this extends to both patients and every member of the team. If you spend more than a few days at a practice, bringing in some biscuits or cake for the receptionists on the last day will always leave you in the good books and likely get you a return invite the next time they need a locum!

Useful contacts:
National Association of Sessional GPs (NASGP) - **www.nasgp.org.uk**

Starting out as a salaried GP

Many doctors spend a large part of their careers working in a salaried capacity. All of us are salaried while we are completing our vocational training schemes. In the last few years, partnership opportunities have been reduced, and many more qualified GPs work as salaried GPs post CCT. This was highlighted in a Pulse survey that showed that in 2008, 66% of GP job ads were for salaried vacancies, while in 2009, 80% of ads were for salaried vacancies.[1]

There are many benefits of being salaried, which were explored earlier in this guide.

This section looks into the terms of the model BMA contract for salaried GPs in more detail, as well as offering some advice on salaried GP jobs in general.

Who is a salaried GP?

The term salaried GP is applied to a wide range work patterns and practice settings. The umbrella term includes:

- Full time or part time salaried GP in a GMS, PMS, PCTMS, or APMS practice
- Salaried GP with Specialist Interest
- GP retainee
- Flexible Career Scheme GP
- OOH Salaried GP
- GP assistant / associate
- GP returner

Model BMA contract

The model BMA contract for salaried GPs provides guidelines on the *minimum* terms and conditions that can be offered for salaried GPs working in GMS or PCO run practices. It covers pay, annual leave, CPD, and rights in relation to sick and maternity pay. GMS and PCO practice are contractually bound to offer terms at least as good as the BMA model contract. Despite this, many GMS practices still offer contracts that are significantly less favourable. Practices face tough sanctions for doing this (although the sanctions are rarely enforced). Sanctions for GMS practices include the loss of the GMS contract (this is outlined in Schedule 6, part 4, paragraph 115 of the directions). If a PCT is not offering the BMA model contract then the Health Department can send an instruction to force implementation.

If you are working in a PCO or GMS practice and have concerns about the contract being offered, you could discuss this with the BMA or an employment lawyer for advice.

BMA model contract – an overview

Hours
Under the terms of the BMA contract, a full time salaried GP would work no more than 37.5 hours. This is made up of 9 notional sessions each lasting 4 hours and 10 minutes. A minimum of 1 session of the 9 should be for CPD, although this can be averaged out over the year. Part time entitlements are calculated pro rata. Any additional hours (including extended hours) should be by mutual agreement with additional pay or time off in lieu.

Annual leave

The minimum leave to be offered should be 30 working days minimum + 10 statutory / public holidays. This is made up of 8 bank holidays + 2 NHS days which can be taken any time. Many employers do not provide the 2 additional NHS days, so you should check this in your contract. Annual leave for a part time GP is calculated pro rata.

Salary

The recommended salary range for a full time salaried GP according to the BMA model contract is £53,249 to £80,354. There is no actual upper limit as practices can offer as much as they like. The model contract mandates that the pay must be uplifted each year according to DDRB recommendations, although there is no incremental increase as in training grades. The salary range for a part time doctor is pro rate, using 9 sessions as full time.

Job Plan

Having a job plan is an essential part of your contact, and this should outline your normal duties – how many surgeries, length of surgeries, on call commitment, house visits etc. The expected workload should be covered, although it is understood that is may vary over the year. Any non clinical duties in working time should also be outlined and specified.

Continuing Professional Development

The model contract requires that you be offered a minimum of 4 hours CPD time each week (annualised) – this equates to 1 session per week. This can be accrued and taken in blocks for study leave to attend courses. The CPD requirement can include protected teaching time organised by the practice or the PCO.

Other leave

Maternity leave

The current entitlement according to the model contract is:

- 8 weeks full pay
- 14 weeks half pay
- 26 weeks unpaid leave

You need 12 months continuous NHS service to qualify for this level of maternity pay. Currently the GPC is pursuing a change in the model contract to put maternity leave in line with hospital terms and conditions which are more generous than this.

Sick leave

Your sick leave entitlement will vary according to your total continuous NHS service, and starts from 1 month full pay and 2 months half pay after 1 year, rising to 6 months full pay and 6 months half pay after more than 5 years continuous NHS service.

Contracts for non GMS / PCO practices

PMS and APMS practices are not bound by the BMA model contract, and can offer any contract they wish. They do have to offer certain minimums imposed under the European Working Time Directive and under UK law. This includes a minimum of 4 weeks annual leave, and minimum rest provisions. There is no minimum salary (except the UK minimum wage!). There is no requirement to offer any annual pay rise, and no pay protection. Remember that all contracts are negotiable, and you do not have to settle for the initial offer. You may be able to negotiate a better package as a whole, especially if you are flexible – for example you might agree to a lower salary if the practice pays for your indemnity and offers more CPD or annual leave. Some PMS practices do offer the BMA model contract.

Employment rights

As mentioned earlier, a big advantage of being an employee is the provision of employment rights, and this applies regardless of the type of practice you are working for. Any employee will acquire full employment rights after 1 yr in job with relation to unfair dismissal. You will be eligible for redundancy after 2 years (where a redundancy situation arises). If you are employed on a fixed contract for more than 4 years, your contract will automatically become permanent (whether a new contract is provided or not).

Salaried GP overview

It is important that you have a firm job plan and understand what is expected of you in your role as a salaried GP. Remember that you are not a partner, and so you have clearly defined rights and responsibilities. If you are regularly being asked to work beyond the terms of your contract and job plan, you should discuss a change in work pattern or an increase in pay. Any changes to your contract will usually need to be by mutual agreement.

Further reading:

GPC (2008) Focus on salaried GPs: guidance for GPs. Available online at
**www.londondeanery.ac.uk/general-practice/files/developing-your-career/
focus-on-salaried-gps-revised-april-2008.pdf**

Taking up a GP partnership

Many doctors still aspire to become GP partners at some point in their career. While there are numerous benefits to being a partner (including extra control and greater pay), there are also many drawbacks and extra responsibilities. Many of these were highlighted in the first chapter, now we will look into some aspects you should be aware of when considering taking up a partnership.

Partnership agreements

A partnership agreement is a legal document that sets out the terms of the partnership. It will set out in detail the rights and responsibilities of the partners as well as specifying how disputes will be dealt with. It is an essential part of any successful practice. Any partnership that does not have a valid partnership agreement will become in effect a "partnership at will":

*"Without a written **partnership agreement**, a 'partnership at will' will almost certainly be in existence, and the relationship between partners will be governed by the provisions of the **Partnership** Act 1890. A practice without a written **partnership agreement** is an unstable business arrangement."* GPC 2004

Despite this, around 50% of partnerships operate without a valid partnership agreement. Entering a partnership like this is risky because in a partnership at will, any partner can terminate the partnership without any notice without needing any reason. This could mean that the practice contract could be terminated, lead to the forced sale of all assets, the redundancy of all employees as well as huge legal costs and a lot of stress. When considering a partnership it is essential to see the existing agreement, and to discuss any changes to be made before a new one is drawn up to include details of the new partner.

Important areas in the partnership agreement

Partners
The agreement should state who the partners making up the partnership are, as well as each partner's workload (number of sessions, clinical / non clinical).

Parity and profit sharing
The parity of each partner and their respective profit shares, as well as how this is to be calculated should be outlined in details. This should include the method used to allocate private income (e.g. from insurance medicals), seniority payments, and the time taken to parity for new partners.

Ownership of premises and valuation
Details of who owns the premises, and how the any valuation for the premises should be calculated in the event that a partner leaves the partnership and the remaining members wish to buy out their share of the equity in the premises.

Leave

As partners are not employees, they do not automatically have a right to any set minimum amount of any form of leave. Any provisions for leave, including the amounts available, whether paid or unpaid should be specified in the agreement. This should include details of annual leave, sick leave, study leave, maternity and paternity leave.

Dissolution and disagreements

Unfortunately sometimes partners have disagreements, and this can lead to dissolution – a breakup of the partnership. By outlining which events will lead to dissolution, and how disagreements will be handled (e.g. by involving an independent mediator); a lot of stress and expense can be saved in the event things don't work out. It is also sensible to include minimum notice periods for dissolving a practice.

Parity

Parity in a partnership determines how profits will be distributed amongst the partners. If all partners have equal (or full) parity, then they will share the profits equally if they all work an equal number of sessions. It is common for incoming partners to sometimes start on lower parity to reflect the fact that the other partners will be shouldering more of the responsibility in terms of the management aspects of running a practice. The time taken to full parity can vary – in some areas new partners will have full parity as soon as they start, in others it may take anywhere from a year to over three years to achieve full parity. Your parity will affect how much income you have, so it is important to understand this. Let us look at a case study to make this clearer:

Case Study: Understanding Parity

Dr Jones applies for a partnership in a 3 Partner practice that does not own the surgery premises. All partners work full time (9 sessions). The senior partner is retiring, and the new incoming partner will work full time. Dr Jones is offered 80% parity in the first year, 90% in year 2 and 100% parity in year 3.

The practice makes a profit of £280,000 each year in the first three years after Dr Jones joins. The profits would be allocated in the following way:

Partner	Income Yr1	Income Yr2	Income Yr3
Partner 1	£100,000 (100% parity)	£96,552 (100% parity)	£93,333 (100% parity)
Partner 2	£100,000 (100% parity)	£96,552 (100% parity)	£93,333 (100% parity)
Dr Jones	£80,000 (80% parity)	£86,896 (90% parity)	£93,333 (100% parity)

Practice Accounts

When entering a partnership, you will be a partner in running a business, not an employee. This means that you will not have a fixed salary, but will be able to draw an income from the profits that the practice makes. Your income can fluctuate from year to year, and can go down as well as up. It is important that you examine the practice finances to understand how the practice is doing, and what your potential income might be. You should request to see at least the last three years of practice accounts. It is worth investing some time and effort to learn the basics of practice accounts for yourself, but you should also get a suitably qualified medical accountant to look through the accounts in full and explain them to you. Ideally this should be an independent accountant (not the accountants the practice use). If a practice refuses to show a potential partner the practice accounts, then it is probably better to steer clear of them – there may be financial problems or issues with management.

Buying into a partnership

When joining any partnership, the incoming partner will have to "buy in" to the partnership. The amount that you will need to pay will vary greatly depending on whether or not the partnership owns the practice premises. Where the practice owns the property, you may be offered the chance to buy into the ownership of the property – how much will depend on the valuation of the property, but this could be several hundred thousand pounds. On top of this, any new partner will need to buy into the current account – this is the money tied up in the other assets the partnership owns, and could include things like furniture, equipment, computers, drugs, and other items necessary for the day to day running of the practice. This is usually a much smaller amount – from a few thousand to a few tens of thousands of pounds depending on the size of the practice. You will need to go through the accounts to determine if the amount you are asked to pay to buy into the current account is accurate. The amount should be equal to the amount stated in the accounts divided by the number of partners. It is currently illegal to try to charge incoming partners for "goodwill" or the value in having established the practice and made it profitable. If you have any doubts with regards to the amount you are asked to pay, ask a specialist accountant to go through this with you.

Partnership Summary

Becoming a partner is a large, long term commitment. It requires a large degree of trust between the partners for it to work, and there should always be a period of mutual assessment before committing to becoming a partner. A period between six months and a year is common.

Before entering a partnership, there are a lot of factors you need to consider in detail – who are the other partners? Who owns the premises? What responsibilities will you need to take on as a partner? Are the terms in the partnership agreement reasonable? How much will you have to pay to buy in? How long will it take to reach full parity? Are the practice finances sound?

Being a partner in the right partnership can be fulfilling, and rewarding both professionally and financially. Being in the wrong partnership can be a source of emotional and financial distress. It is therefore essential that you research the partnership extensively before making a commitment.

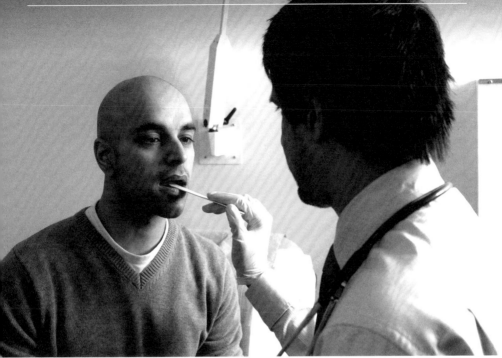

Becoming a Portfolio GP

You may have heard the term "portfolio GP" more frequently over the last few years. This is an umbrella term used to describe any GP that has multiple jobs or that does multiple types of work within their working week. Most portfolio GPs have a primary job – this could be a partnership, a part time salaried position or being a locum GP, with one or more additional jobs in their portfolio.

Many GPs develop a portfolio over time almost by accident – what starts as a one off extra session working in a prison for example can become an interesting part of the working week.

In this chapter we will look at a few of the popular additional jobs that you might develop an interest in as part of your portfolio:

- Medical Education
- Forensic Medical Examiner
- Prison Doctor

Medical Education

There are various ways to become involved in medical education, from the occasional teaching and supervision of medical students on placement at the practice to becoming GP trainers or Training Programme Directors. Teaching can be very rewarding, as well as acting as a stimulus to refresh your own knowledge and to keep up to date.

Teaching Medical Students and Foundation Trainees

Most medical schools require doctors that will be teaching students on placement to attend a short training course (often over 1 or 2 days), and then to attend annual training days. Beyond this, you will not need to have any formal medical education qualifications. For teaching Foundation trainees, most deaneries require a similar amount of training.

Clinical Tutor

Many medical schools recruit qualified GPs to become clinical tutors to facilitate small group teaching, or teach clinical and communication skills for undergraduates at the medical school. Having experience in teaching will make you a more attractive candidate, and medical schools often offer further in house training as well as support to complete a postgraduate certificate or diploma in medical education. Time requirements are usually 1-2 sessions a week.

GP Trainer

The requirements to become a GP trainer vary by deanery, although there are some requirements that are fairly common throughout:

MRCGP – either by examination or via portfolio

Training in teaching – either a trainers' course or a postgraduate certificate or diploma in medical education.

Experience – the minimum post CCT experience varies but usually you will need at least 2-3 years experience as a qualified GP.

There are also requirements that need to be met in relation to the training practice. A trainer would usually need to put aside the equivalent of 2 sessions a week to allow time for supervision, tutorials and ongoing workshops for trainers.

Training Programme Director

Programme Directors (formerly known as VTS Course Organisers) have responsibility for organising the regular teaching for Speciality Training schemes, as well as supporting trainers. Programme Directors are usually appointed via deaneries, and again requirements vary across the county, although most require experience of teaching and a formal postgraduate qualification in medical education at diploma or Masters level. Many Programme Directors are experienced trainers. The time commitment required is usually equivalent to 2 sessions a week or more. In many areas with larger training schemes, there are multiple Programme Directors for the same area.

Forensic Medical Examiner

Forensic Medical Examiners (formerly Police Surgeons) work with police forces to provide assessment and treatment to victims of crime and persons in custody. Many FMEs are GPs that work with the police as an additional role. The work can be interesting and varied[2], and will include assessment and treatment of injuries, minor illness, sudden illness in custody, and assessment of victims of sexual assault. Most FMEs work as part of a group of doctors that provide cover for one or more police stations day and night. A lot of the time you may be able to be on call from home, with extra fees payable for each visit to the station. Another aspect of the work of the FME involves giving evidence in court.

Initial training usually lasts a week, and the training is organised by the host police force, or in some cases private companies contracted by the police force. Costs for training vary from being provided free to around £800. Once the training is complete, doctors will usually be contracted to work on a self employed basis, with payments for being on call, and extra payments for each visit to the station for assessments, for completing reports, and for each attendance at court.

There is an ongoing requirement to keep up to date, with at least 24 hours of CPD in clinical forensic medicine. While being an FME can be exciting, it is also very challenging, and will not suit everyone.

2   See www.pulsetoday.co.uk/story.asp?storycode=4117127 for details

Prison Doctor

There are currently over 140 prisons in the UK, and every single one requires cover from clinicians to look after the welfare of the inmates. In many prisons, regular surgery sessions are offered by GPs from local practices that have contracted to offer cover. Most prisons will also require sessional and on call cover from GPs on a freelance basis.

GPs do not need to have any extra qualifications to work in prisons, although having the RCGP Drug Misuse Management Certificate Part 1 is advantageous and may mean you are more employable.

The work is similar to working in practice, although you may have additional security present or nearby when consulting with certain patients. A larger proportion of your patients may have mental health needs, and a significant proportion may be using or have used illicit drugs. You may also need to assess inmates with injuries, and where necessary arrange for transfers to hospital for further care. Prison work can be very challenging, but also offers an opportunity to improve the healthcare of vulnerable patients. One thing it won't be is boring![3]

---

3   See www.pulsetoday.co.uk/story.asp?storyCode=4012432&sectioncode=21 for details

GP Career Options Summary

In this guide we have looked at a handful of the many options open to the qualified GP. We have explored in detail the most common options. Hopefully you now have a better understanding of what might suit you as well as some of the issues you will need to consider for each type of GP job.

These are just a few of the options – other options include medicolegal assessments, working as an occupational health physician or school doctor, becoming a sports team doctor, a race track doctor or doing medical assessments for divers, and many more. If you have a passion or interest in any field of medicine, there is usually a way to incorporate it into your working life as a GP, either as your main job or as an addition to your portfolio. This is one of the best aspects of working in general practice – there is a lot of flexibility in how you shape your career.

Whichever path you choose to follow, remember that no career choice is better or worse than another – it is about finding the one that fits with your life and aspirations, and this itself may be very fluid. What might suit you really well immediately after qualifying may be different to what meets your needs 5 or 10 years later. You may have different responsibilities, different attitudes and even different interests.

I wish you every success in finding YOUR perfect job, and hope you enjoy the journey to find it as much as the job itself!

Reducing your medicolegal
risk in practice

In this chapter, Sara Williams and Dr Richard Stacey from the MPS outline
things you can do to make sure that you are practicing safely, and reducing
the risk of complaints and medicolegal problems as a qualified GP.

Communicate effectively

Being able to communicate effectively is one of the most important skills of a GP. The successful application of your clinical skills depends on good communication with patients and colleagues.

Understandably patients experience difficulties in assessing the technical competency of a doctor, so will frequently judge the quality of clinical competence by their interpersonal interactions with a doctor. Developing good communication skills will improve clinical effectiveness and reduce medicolegal risk.

It is often said that body language speaks louder than words and it has often been suggested 80% of communication is non-verbal. A mismatch between verbal and non-verbal communication can lead to a strained encounter for both doctors and their patients. Being aware of your own body language is the first step in understanding how it is perceived.

Tips for effective non-verbal communication:

- Observe
- Show respect
- Be patient
- Be self aware (posture, eye contact, first impression)
- Be curious
- Assess patients' moods
- Show empathy.

Part of communicating effectively is managing expectations. Patients will be dissatisfied if their expectations have not been met. Sometimes these expectations may be unrealistic, which makes it all the more important to identify and manage them at the earliest possible stage. So, once explored and respectfully corrected through effective communication, the patient will leave content with their treatment and more likely to comply with it.

Take consent properly

Patients are now better informed, more demanding and want to be more closely involved with their treatment. Good consent facilitates this process. So it is not only good practice to be familiar with consent guidance, but the GMC will judge your practice against it, which could have a bearing on your career.

Consent must be freely given by a competent patient voluntarily making an informed decision. Consent is about more than a single decision; rather it is a process to inform the patient of the nature and purpose of their condition and its treatment (and to ensure that they have understood the information that has been provided).

Consent must fulfil three conditions to be valid. The patient must be:

- capable of giving consent
- sufficiently informed to make a considered decision
- giving consent voluntarily.

If you are providing treatment, it is your responsibility to obtain consent. If you are asked to get consent for a particular treatment you should only do so if you are familiar with the procedure and sufficiently informed to answer a patient's questions accurately.

Don't breach confidentiality

In a GP practice, where you are closely involved with the local community and have an ongoing relationship with patients, maintaining the trust of patients is vital. In today's team-driven environment, communication has to extend to a greater number of people, so there are more opportunities for it to fail.

Communication between primary, secondary, voluntary and social care should be viewed not as a chain but as a communication net, where all members can contact each other. This requires all members to be aware of who is doing what and understand the part they play. This will inevitably involve sharing patient information, which is entirely appropriate as long as continuity of care is balanced with the need to maintain confidentiality.

In its latest confidentiality guidance, the GMC says that most people understand and accept that information must be shared within the healthcare team in order to provide their care. But it is not always clear how that information will be used. So patients should be informed about disclosures for purposes other than what they would expect. If a patient objects to the disclosure, you should explain that you cannot refer them or otherwise arrange for their treatment without also disclosing that information.

Keep good medical records

In a busy GP practice, where patients can see a number of different health professionals or be referred to colleagues in secondary care, it is essential that records are accurate and up-to-date.

You are professionally obliged to keep good records. In the event of a complaint, clinical negligence claim or disciplinary proceedings, the medical record will contain the factual base for your defence. Cases can be difficult to defend if information is missing, inaccurate or indecipherable.

Good medical records include any information created by, or on behalf of, a health professional in connection with the care of a patient. They can cover a wide range of material:

- Handwritten medical notes
- Computerised records
- Correspondence between health professionals
- Laboratory reports
- X-ray films and other imaging records
- Photographs
- Videos and other recordings
- Printouts from monitoring equipment
- Text messages
- Emails.

Correspondence relating to complaints or claims should be filed separately, as they are not part of the patient's medical record.

Do not change the original medical record unless the information is factually incorrect. If you discover a mistake, insert an additional note as a correction. Make it clear that this is a new note, not an attempt to tamper with the original record.

In a busy practice, your contact with patients is not limited to consultations in the surgery. There will also be:

- Home visits
- Out-of-hours work
- Telephone consultations
- Impromptu requests from practice staff to "have a quick word" with a patient.

Medical records should be kept in a secure environment. That means restricting access to authorised personnel and ensuring that records are kept physically safe. You should consider issues such as:

- Fire precautions – an alarm system, chemical fire extinguishers (do not use a sprinkler system as water can be even more damaging than fire) and no smoking signs.
- Keeping important paper documents in a fire-proof safe, but do not entrust your computer back-up drive to a fire-proof safe – use secure, off-site storage instead.
- Preventing damage from damp, flooding or pests.
- Staff awareness of duty to prevent unauthorised disclosure.
- Passwords, encryption software and restricted access for staff.
- Repairs – ensure these are carried out on the premises or in a secure environment with a confidential agreement.

Handle complaints correctly

Should you receive a complaint, you might wish to talk to an experienced colleague or your medical defence organisation. The complaint should be dealt with in accordance with the NHS Complaints Procedure, which requires you to:

- Acknowledge the complaint
- Find out the facts
- Provide an explanation
- Apologise where appropriate
- Identify what can be done to prevent similar issues arising
- Adopt those lessons in your future practice.

How can MPS help?

GPs have their own particular needs, so MPS offers a flexible service to meet them. Subscriptions reflect the variety of work undertaken by GPs – so they only pay the amount appropriate for the professional protection they require.

MPS can assist GPs with:

- Handling complaints
- Attendance at Coroner's inquests (or fatal accident inquiries)
- Disciplinary matters
- Criminal matters
- General medicolegal advice
- Media enquiries
- Good Samaritan acts (anywhere in the world).

MPS provides a wealth of medicolegal information and education, both in publications and on its website. In addition to *Casebook*, the signature journal of MPS, GPs receive *Your Practice*, a quarterly magazine that tackles medicolegal problems commonly encountered by the whole practice team, and *Sessional GP*, an annual magazine for locum GPs.

Sara Williams works as a writer and editor and Richard Stacey is a GP and a medicolegal adviser for MPS.

Meeting your needs as a newly qualified GP

Starting work as a newly-qualified GP will be a rewarded experience. But working autonomously can present its own challenges. You are not alone MPS Can provide assistance during this time to help you enjoy your first year as a GP.

Summary of benefits once you qualify as a GP

Once you come to the end of your GP training programme, we will continue to support you by providing you with access to:

- Educational support – this doesn't stop once your complete your training, there is always the need to improve your knowledge and skills, to reduce your risk of litigation and contribute to safer practice
- Keycard with instant access to contact numbers

- Discounted subscription rates in your first year as a GP, call the membership department on **0845 718 7187** to find out more
- Newly qualified GP pack – an invaluable resource that will aid you throughout your GP career
- Practice reward package scheme if you are working in a practice
- Flexible membership rates if you work as a sessional GP
- Advice service – our medicolegal advice service is open to members with urgent enquiries 24 hours a day.

To find out more about how MPS can support you in your first year as a GP or how to join MPS please visit **www.mps.org.uk/gp** or call us on **0845 718 7187.**

GP Jobs Directory – Useful Resources

In this section I have listed some useful resources that you may find helpful in looking for a job. All these links and any updates are available at www.gpjobs.org for easy navigation.

Job Hunting – all career options

Pulse - Weekly GP magazine with daily job updates on website. Large number of jobs, easy to navigate and search. www.pulsetoday.co.uk

Healthcare Republic - Weekly GP magazine with daily job updates on website. Large number of jobs, easy to navigate and search. www.healthcarerepublic.com

BMJ Careers – Weekly journal has a GP specific edition, with a good number of jobs. Website very easy to navigate and search for specific jobs. www.careers.bmj.com

BJGP – Monthly journal for members of the Royal College of General Practitioners. Paper version usually has a good number of substantive post. Website design is very poor, with poor navigation and very difficult to search for specific job types. www.rcgp.org.uk/publications/bjgp.aspx

GP Locum Agencies – United Kingdom

Name	Notes	Website
Ambition 24Locums	Nationwide, GP, OOH	www.a24locum.co.uk
CB Locums	Nationwide, GP, Military, Prison	www.cblocums.com
Connect Locums	Nationwide, GP, OOH, Prison	www.connectlocums.com
Dr Locums	Nationwide, GP, OOH, Prison	www.drlocums.com
Fresh Medical	Nationwide, GP, OOH	www.freshmedical.com
Locum Link	UK and Ireland, GP	www.locumlink.ie
Locum Staffing	Nationwide, GP, OOH, Prison	www.locumstaffing.co.uk
Medacs	Nationwide, GP, OOH, Prison, FME	www.medacs.com
Medteam	Nationwide, GP, OOH, Prison	www.medteam.co.uk
Military Medical Personnel	Nationwide, International, Military bases	www.militarymedicalpersonnel.com
Team24	Nationwide, GP, OOH, Prison	www.team24.co.uk

A complete directory with links is available at www.gpjobs.org

International GP Jobs – Recruitment Agencies

Name	Region	Website
Actualise Australia	Australia	www.actualiseaust.com
Beat Medical	Australia	www.beatmedical.com
Health Match BC	British Columbia, Canada	www.healthmatchbc.org
Health Staff Recruitment	Australia, New Zealand	www.healthstaffrecruitment.com.au
NSW Rural Doctors Network	New South Wales, Australia	www.nswrdn.com.au
Ochre Medical Recruitment	Australia, New Zealand	www.ochrerecruitment.com.au
Pulse International	Australia, New Zealand, Canada, Middle East	www.pulsejobs.com
Rural Doctors Workforce Agency	Rural South Australia	www.ruraldoc.com.au
Triple0 Medical Recruitment	Australia, New Zealand	www.triple0.com
Wavelength International	Australia, New Zealand, Canada	www.wave.com.au

A complete directory with links is available at **www.gpjobs.org**